A Ship Under Sail

A 17th Century Sailor

THE OCEAN JOURNEY

DOWN CLUES:

1. Largest of the three ships which brought the English to Jamestown.

2. Term which refers to lowest ranking sailors.

3. To send goods to another country for sale.

4. Measurement of East/West position on the globe.

5. Sailor in charge of mariners.

ACROSS CLUES:

1. Disease which results from a lack of vitamin C.

6. Middle-sized ship which brought English to Jamestown in 1607.

7. Sea which surrounds islands often visited by English sailors, off the coast of the United States.

8. Large piece of wood which gives a ship much of its strength.

9. Rear of the ship.

10. Bringing goods from other countries into your country.

11. North/South position on the globe.

12. Front of the ship.

SHIPS AND SAILING

```
S M E V C O M P A S S N D N I U G
Q U J H J O T B R E O O A O C F T
P D S A I L O R S Y H I L S J Z W
R O B A G X B L E C J T W I N D E
T I E O N P C N Y U M A J Y K W E
U N H U Q C E O L R T G F E A C N
V C B P I X O V I R E I M Z U Y D
V D P F C K A N B E X V R P D I E
A H O L D B U R S N H A O H Q F C
M K S K N F S P A T C N J C U A K
Q R V A Y L B K P S A L B Y S B Q
P Y M D E E P S D O G N G I E I U
L E S V W A C M R F J E T R X S D
```

The words in this word search puzzle go up, down, and diagonally. As you find each word, cross it off the list.

Susan Constant	**Hold**	**Compass**
Godspeed	**Tween Deck**	**Wind**
Discovery	**Sailors**	**Currents**

Using the wordlist below and the hints in the drawing, see if you can fill in the blanks and name the parts of the ship.

1. This is a diagram of the A. _____, the largest of the three ships that brought settlers to Jamestown.

2. The B. _____ is using a C. _____ on the D. _____.

3. The E. _____ rings every half hour.

4. This is the F. _____.

5. The G. _____ is in the H. _____.

6. The I. _____ is in the J. _____.

7. The passengers lived in the K. _____.

8. Most supplies were stored in the L. _____.

9. Daily food and water came from the M. _____.

10. The front of the ship is called the N. _____.

WORDLIST:

Bow, Captain, Cook, Cross Staff, Forecastle, Great Cabin, Hold, Main Mast, Navigator, Quarter Deck, Ships Bell, Storage Room, Susan Constant, Tween Deck

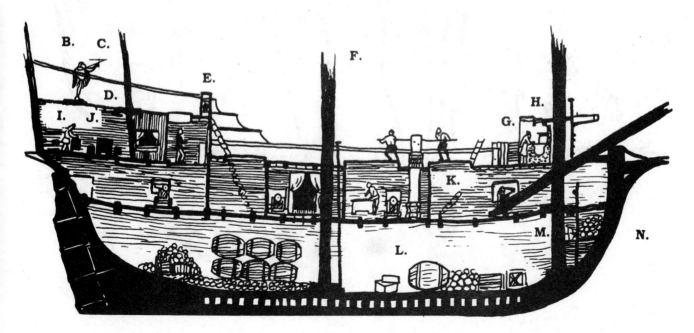

5

An Indian Maiden

6

An Indian Warrior

An Indian Meal

Building a Canoe

Indians Cooking Fish

POWHATAN INDIANS

DOWN:

1. An Indian trade item very much needed by the English.

2. Famous Indian girl whose marriage to John Rolfe helped relations between the Powhatans and the colonists.

3. Name of the Bay along which the Powhatans lived.

4. Animal which provided the Indians with food, clothing, tools, and other useful items.

5. Soft metal that was a highly valued trade item.

6. Common Indian food made from corn.

7. Food gathered by Powhatans.

ACROSS:

3. Customs, traditions, and way of life of a group of people.

8. Powhatan Indian god who punished people for wrongdoing.

9. A building where Indian boys were taught about their tribe.

10. A string made from the tendons and ligaments of deer.

11. The way Powhatan Indians obtained most of their food.

12. These were woven into mats for longhouses.

13. Article of clothing worn by Powhatan Indians.

14. Title of the ruler of the Powhatan Indians.

15. Material used to make many tools including arrowheads.

16. Powhatan Indian word for house.

Draw a line to match the pictures on the left with pictures on the right.

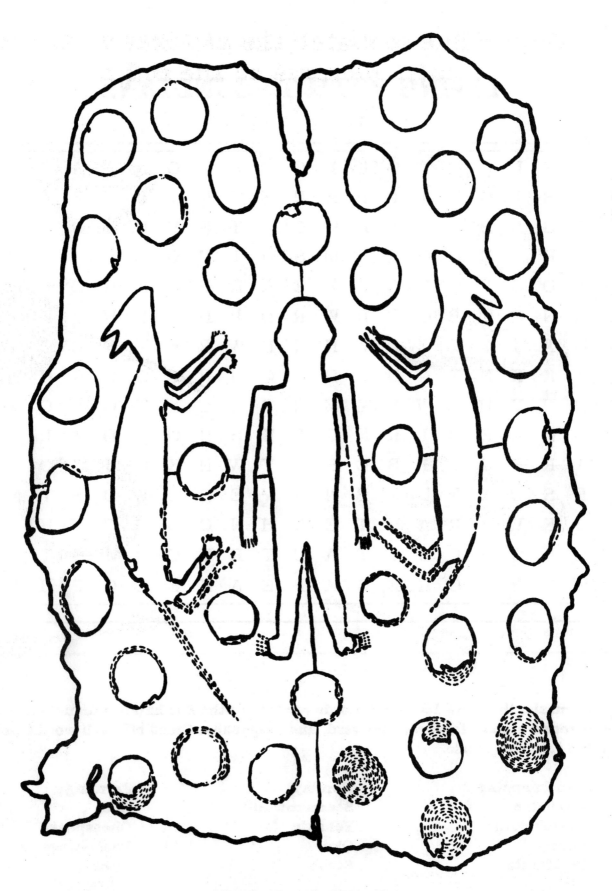

Powhatan's Mantle
A decorated ceremonial cape which may have belonged to the ruler
of Virginia's Powhatan Indian chiefdom in the early 17th century.

LIVING WITH THE INDIANS

```
R F L Q M S G F P O C A H O N T A S W
A B T G N I P P A N K T N I L F Z A Z
E G L B X B S H W O T T S V U V N B N
F H L D C O R N M S N I U D T K J R M
A D O P Q V C X L E X R P U D G D E P
R N Q M P O Z R W R D P H L Y H E E O
M X J W I Z O W H N E W R E Y F E C W
I K K N X N D F R V O N H C G S G H H
N N Y H C W Y Z M R P A E M T G N C A
G D E E R I R H C P K B N O F D U L T
I R F G P I B E B I V W N K G J T O A
E S L N F B R B N T V E Q L E D S T N
J K V J R A N T E C H N O L O G Y H L
G K O B C S I T A U T R T C B J S T S
W O H S C H E S A P E A K E E O P H A
```

In this puzzle, there are 15 hidden words relating to the Powhatan Indians. The words can be found across, forward, backward, and diagonally. Cross off each word below as you find it in the puzzle.

Flintknapping	Hominy	Farming
Powhatan	Scarecrow Hut	Deer
Breechcloth	Yehakin	Chesapeake
Corn	Oke	Technology
Pocahontas	Stone	Nuts

Connect the dots and answer the question.

Who is this famous Indian woman?

_____

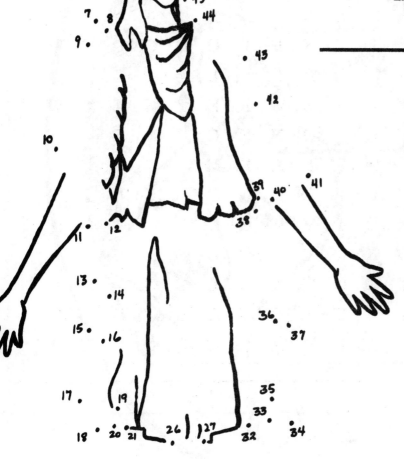
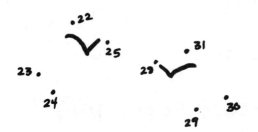

Pocahontas in about the year 1616

Draw lines and identify these Indian objects.

Oyster Shells

Bone Implements

Projectile Points

Axe Head

Stone Pendent

Clay Pot

CORN "MAIZE"

Start

Finish

18

POWHATAN INDIANS AND ENGLISH SETTLERS

ACROSS CLUES:

1. Protective headgear worn by English soldier.
7. Important English weapon.
10. Daughter of Powhatan.
11. The Atlantic _____ separated Virginia and England.
12. The Powhatans thought an English _____ was like a moving island.
14. The animal whose fur was desired by the English to make hats.
16. To _____: Wool blankets and metal tools for corn and beaver pelts.
18. The most important Powhatan farm product.
19. The people who came to Jamestown in 1607.
24. Metal disk worn at the neck; Wahunsunacock wore a copper one.
25. Container for arrows.
26. An English one was metal and sharp; Indians wanted one.
27. Pocahontas was a _____ of the English settlers.

DOWN CLUES:

1. Gardening tool. English had metal ones; Powhatans may have used a sea shell.
2. Powhatan shoes.
3. Primary material used to make Powhatan clothing.
4. The skills, arts, customs, behavior of a group of people at a given time.
5. Social ranking based on wealth or title.
6. After Pocahontas married John Rolfe, there was a time of _____.
8. A Powhatan warrior would _____ the side of his head with clam shells.
9. Share ideas by talking and gesturing.
10. The native Americans living in Tidewater, Virginia in 1607.
13. A Powhatan body decoration.
14. Important Powhatan weapon.
15. Powhatan transportation.
17. Language spoken by Powhatan.
20. English _____ were wattle and daub; Powhatan's were of bent samplings and woven mats.
21. Powhatans were _____ along the rivers when the English came.
22. Used to make many Indian tools.
23. A stone axe.

Find the 11 animals and then color the picture.

A 17th Century Pikeman

"James Fort" was built from May 14 to June 15, 1607.

SEARCHING FOR HERBS

```
R X P Y R R U C E D A G
N Y A C H A M O M I L E
O L R I N S U R T L L M
R C S N B A S I L L I T
F H L N A G T A R E N U
F I E A N E A N S M A N
A V Y M O U R D E O V O
S E V O L C D E T N O I
E S L N T O S R P E U R
M Y G I N G E R A P H R
P I C K I S E S A M E A
E T H Y M E D L E U M P
```

An important reason why the English wanted to settle in Jamestown was to search for a shortcut to the Pacific Ocean where many popular spices were grown. Saffron and ginger, for instance, came from India. Spices were important as medicine, in food preparation, and for household products. See if you have any at home in your spice cabinet. Some are hidden away in the word search above. See if you can find:

Basil	Chamomile	Chives
Cinnamon	Cloves	Coriander
Curry	Dill	Ginger
Lemon	Mustard Seed	Mint
Nutmeg	Parsley	Pepper
Rue	Saffron	Sage
Sesame	Thyme	Vanilla

This settler has lost his way in the woods.
Can you help him find his way back to Jamestown before the night settles in and it is too dark to find his home?

Jamestown

Start

"James Towne" in 1619

Captain John Smith

LIFE AT JAMESTOWN

ACROSS CLUES:

1. Winter of 1609-10 when so many settlers died.

5. Leader who improved conditions at Jamestown.

7. Animals raised for food.

8. Native American crop grown by Indians as main food.

10. As John Smith explored, he drew these.

11. Native American chiefdom located in area of Jamestown in 1607.

13. Main reason Virginia Company came to new world was to make a _____.

16. Very harsh rules in Jamestown 1610-1614.

17. The Virginia _____ sold stock to earn money to finance Jamestown.

18. Plants grown and dried to be used in cooking and as medicine.

DOWN CLUES:

2. Crop grown by settlers that made a profit.

3. Upper-class Englishman who was not used to working with his hands.

4. Water in the James River contains salt and so it is called _____.

5. Man responsible for the cultivation of tobacco at Jamestown.

6. Indian girl who was a friend to the English.

9. English King who granted the charter for Jamestown.

12. The enemy that concerned the English when they built the fort.

14. Jamestown was actually on a peninsula, not an _____.

15. Every man in Jamestown wore some kind of _____ to protect themselves in case of an attack.

Glass making was one of America's first industries.

Draw a line to match the Jamestown industry with the craftsmen.

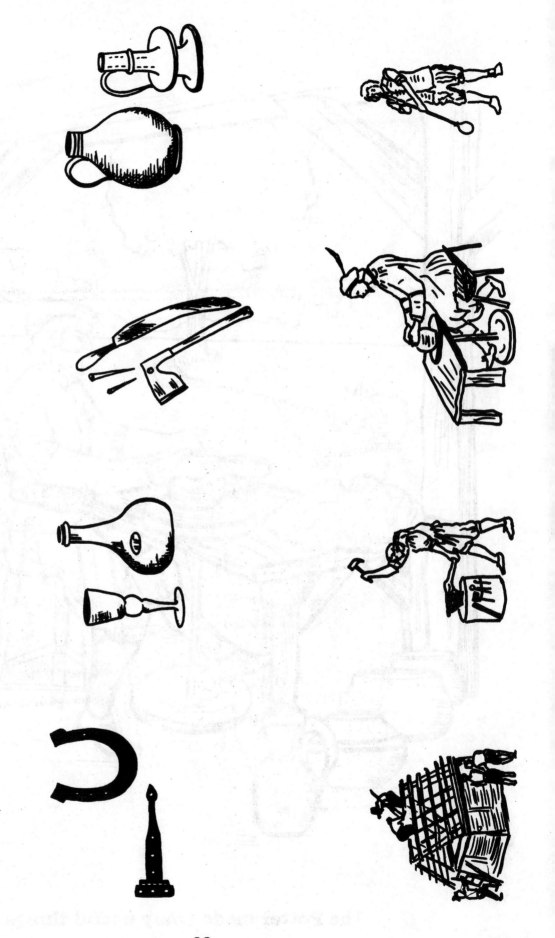

The Potter made many useful things.

Artifacts or "Old Things"

Objects that people leave behind can tell us how they lived. The objects made or used by man are called artifacts. Use this list and see if you can identify the 10 artifacts.

Pottery Jug   Candlestick
Scissors   Spoon
Horseshoe   Carpenter's Tools
Iron Hoe   Thimble
Pile Driver   Cutlass

6.

3.

5.

7.

1.

10.

4.

9.

2.

8.

1. _____   6. _____

2. _____   7. _____

3. _____   8. _____

4. _____   9. _____

5. _____   10. _____

Harvesting Tobacco

These words are hidden backwards, forwards, diagonally, and vertically in the puzzle. See if you can find them all.

```
B V I R G I N I A C O M P A N Y O F L O N D O N
G E N T L E M E N O U F V S T A R D E N U G W A
P N S U S A N C O N S T A N T O B S E C N T Y Z
O G A T L A N T I C O C E A N R B W C U K I N G
W L V R W L T V N A R S V I H U J A L U N P A T
H A P Q U E B E R T H I S I E D I S C O V E R Y
A N O G O D S P E E D R D I R E S W G C A R T S
T D C O L F O T Q U T R F D S G I K O P O M I D
A S A L A A H B I N D I A N S T I W A T S A F C
N O H D E R S C A N A R Y I S L A N D S M N A H
H J O E D F R S D T D O P L W Y T N I O O E C E
C O N E R T Y I L K O I W A O C A B W A S N T S
R H T A D R O J U T H G E T M O P L A N Q T S A
U N A T I O N A L P A R K S E R V I C E U E R P
H R S T J F U L S T A R V I N G T I M E I Y T E
C O R N A C B R I C K M A K E R T F M O T E P A
A L E R M A E C T R I A N G L E I A A U O T O K
I F R I E R A A W I N L U G G R E A R R W X T E
A E H I S P U N E S G W I N E D R I S N M O T B
V E N I T E N N W E J O H N S M I T H E O E E A
K O T G O N O O I T A A E T F R G Y E D I A R Y
Q U S D W T M N W A M D I S E A S E S J U V D F
S P A I N E D C U H E J A M E S R I V E R O L J
T R H G I R R H O U S E O F B U R G E S S E S A
```

Artifact	Atlantic Ocean	Brickmaker	Canary Islands
Cannon	Carpenter	Chesapeake Bay	Church
Corn	Diary	Discovery	Disease
England	Farmer	Fire	Fort
Gentlemen	Glass	Godspeed	Gold
House of Burgesses	Indians	James River	Jamestown
John Rolfe	John Smith	King James	Marshes
Mosquito	Spain	Permanent	Pocahontas
Powhatan	Tobacco	Starving Time	Susan Constant
Tar	Potter	Triangle	Virginia Company of London
Virginia		Women	West Indies

An Artifact from a Jamestown "Dig"

**A brick house at Jamestown,
built in the late 1600s.**

The first brick church built in Jamestown in 1639.

Jamestown Memorial Cross

Answers to page 3

Answers to page 4

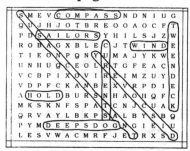

Answers to page 5

Answers to page 17

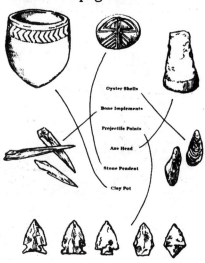

Answers to page 14

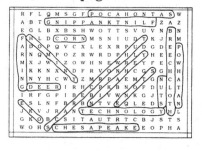

Answers to page 11

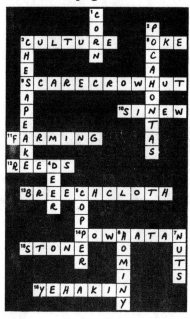

Answers to page 12

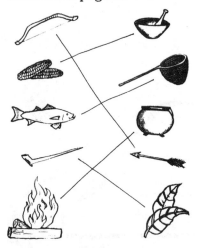

Answers to page 31

1. Horseshoe
2. Cutlass
3. Pile Driver
4. Carpenter's Tools
5. Spoon
6. Scissors
7. Thimble
8. Candlestick
9. Pottery Jug
10. Iron Hoe

Answers to page 19

Answer to page 18

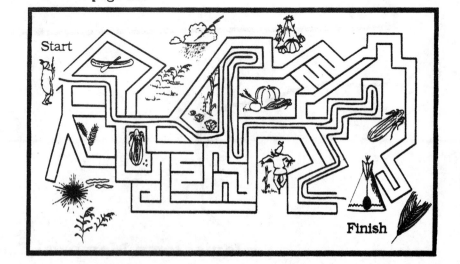

Start

Finish

Answers to page 23

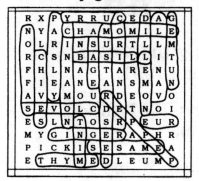

Answer to page 24

Answers to page 27

Answers to page 29

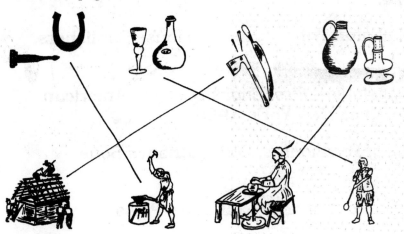

Answers to page 33

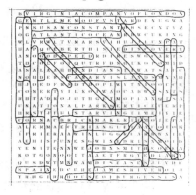

Books to Read for Fun

Billings, Warren M. *Jamestown and the Founding of the Nation.* Thomas Publications, Gettysburg, Pennsylvania, 1991.

Boelt, Martha McDonald. *Chanco Visits Jamestown.* HS Printing and Stationary, Inc., White Stone, Virginia, 1983.

Cambell, Helen J. *The American Sketches for the very Young Present: Chanco, The Indian Hero of Colonial Jamestown.* R.M. Ursy, Williamsburg, Virginia, 1951.

Campbell, Elizabeth A. *Jamestown the Beginning.* Little, Brown and Company, Boston, 1974.

Feest, Christian F. *The Powhatan Tribes.* Chelsea House Publishers, New York, 1990.

Fishwick, Marshall W. *Jamestown—First English Colony.* American Heritage Publishing Co., Inc., New York, 1965.

Fritz, Jean. *The Double Life of Pocahontas.* G.P. Putnam's Sons, New York, 1983.

Johnston, Johanna. *Who Found America?* Children's Press, Chicago, 1973.

Kay, Alan N. *Jamestown Journey.* Thomas Publications, Gettysburg, Pennsylvania, 1992.

McCary, Ben C. and Parke Rouse, Jr. *Virginia Indians Before and After Jamestown.* Jamestown Foundation, Jamestown, Virginia.

Percy, George. *Observations Gathered Out of "A Discourse of the Plantation of the Southern Colony in Virginia by the English, 1606."* University Press of Virginia, Charlottesville, 1967.

Prolman, Marilyn. *The Story of Jamestown.* Children's Press, Chicago, 1973.

Seymour, Flora Warren. *Pocahontas, Brave Girl.* Bobbs-Merrill Co., Inc., Indianapolis, Indiana, New York City, New York, 1961.

Smith, John. *The Adventures and Discourses of Captain John Smith.* Reissued by Singing Trees Book Tower, Detroit, 1969.